For Ann and Linda - H.J.
For Darcey - H.T.

BLOOMSBURY CHILDREN'S BOOKS
Bloomsbury Publishing Plc
50 Bedford Square, London, WC1B 3DP, UK

BLOOMSBURY, BLOOMSBURY CHILDREN'S BOOKS and the Diana logo are trademarks of Bloomsbury Publishing Plc

First published in Great Britain 2020 by Bloomsbury Publishing Plc

A catalogue record for this book is available from the British Library

ISBN: HB: 978-1-4088-9920-5; PB: 978-1-5266-1624-1; eBook: 978-1-5266-2020-0

2 4 6 8 10 9 7 5 3 1 (hardback)
2 4 6 8 10 9 7 5 3 1 (paperback)

Printed and bound in China by Leo Paper Products, Heshan, Guangdong

All papers used by Bloomsbury Publishing Plc are natural, recyclable products from wood grown in well managed forests.
The manufacturing processes conform to the environmental regulations of the country of origin

To find out more about our authors and books visit www.bloomsbury.com and sign up for our newsletters

IN THE CITY

Holly James • Hannah Tolson

BLOOMSBURY
CHILDREN'S BOOKS

LONDON   OXFORD   NEW YORK   NEW DELHI   SYDNEY

Let's get ready to go to the city

The **city** is waking up and **everyone** is getting ready to set off for the **day**.

Sun

Map

Oscar and Lucy have
a **map** of the **city**.

What **time** is it? The train is leaving soon and we don't want to be **late!**

Ladder

Clock

What amazing things will you see in the city today?

Let's go on the train

The station is buzzing with hustle and bustle. People run past carrying bags of all shapes and sizes.

TRAIN INFORMATION

TIME	DESTINATION	PLATFORM
9:00	THE CITY	3
9:14	PARIS	10
9:22	NEW YORK	5
9:30	LONDON	7
9:36	TOKYO	12

EXIT

TICKETS

CLOSED.

Newspaper

Suitcase

How many **bags** can you count?

SNACKS

Menu.

INFORMATION

Quick! Get on the train and let's **zoom** into the city.

TOILETS

3

Train driver

Bird

Train conductor

What does Lucy spy from the **train?**

Let's visit the museum

Discover **wild** and **wonderful** things at the **museum**.

T.Rex

Vase

Dinosaurs come to life amid **leafy trees** and **tropical flowers**.

Statues stand **tall** and paintings **smile** at the visitors.

Sculpture

Painting

Shoes

Camera

What interesting **artefacts** can you **spot?**

Let's explore the city

Bright lights **flash** and vehicles **whizz** by. It's a **lively day.**

DANGER

Car

Scooter

Motorbike

STOP

museum PARK

Station

Tourists spin around
and snap **photos.**

BUS

UNDERGROUND

i

SEE the SIGHTS!

MUSEUM   BOAT TRIPS

Taxi

Police officers keep the city moving.

Policeman

Bike

What busy vehicles can Oscar name?

Let's climb the tallest building

Up, up, **UP** to the very top.
We're climbing towards
the clouds.

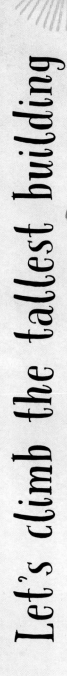

The **SUN** is shining
over the city below.

Tall cranes
stretch
to the sky.

Window
cleaner

Plants

Office

Cat

What can you **find** in the windows?

Let's have a picnic in the park

It's **lunchtime!** Lucy and Oscar are eating their favourite sandwiches. **Yummy! Munch Munch!**

Ice-cream van

Binoculars

Lunch box

Watch the dogs **prance** and **play** in the **park.**

Dog

Bee

How many **ducks** are in the pond?

Let's cruise on the river

All aboard for a **watery adventure!**
The captain **waves** as the engine **roars**
to life and the **boat** sets **sail.**

Plane

Fishing
boat

Ship's
captain

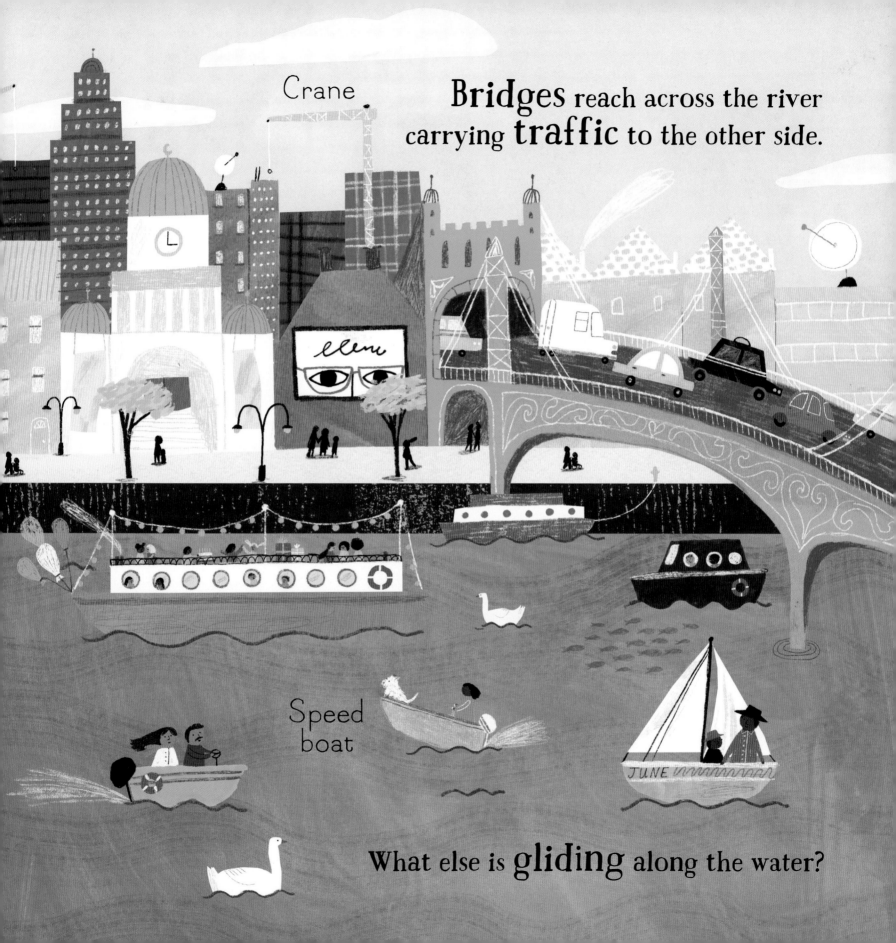

Crane

Bridges reach across the river carrying **traffic** to the other side.

Speed boat

What else is **gliding** along the water?

Let's go shopping

Wander through the **shops** and see what you can find. **Windows** show off colourful clothes and **twinkling treasures.**

GREENFINC

BOOKSHOP

OPEN

Fish

Fruit

Music **plays** through the open doors.

What will you **buy** today?

Let's take a bus tour

Spot all the **sights** as the **bus** zips around the city. Fountains spray **water** through the air in **grand squares**.

Skyscraper

Horse

SEE the SIGHTS!

The city's **skyline** is filled with buildings, **old** and **new**.

TRAIN STATION

Duck

STADIUM

MUSEUM

Fountain

Tourists

Where did Oscar
and Lucy **visit** today?

Let's go home

The sun has set and it's time to go home.
Shutters close on shop doors and the streets
are swept ready for a new day tomorrow.

CARDS & CO.

CLOSED

Brush

Wheelbarrow

The

EXIT

Street lights **glow** as the sky darkens. It's time to get back on the **train**.

luigi's

THEATRE

UNDERGROUND

Light

Underground train

Did you take lots of **photos**?

Let's go to bed

It's been a **busy** day in the city
but now everywhere is **quiet**.

Star

The **city lights twinkle** in the distance.

What did you spot in the city?

Clock

Crane

Museum

Car

House

Bike

Tree

Traffic lights

Train station

Builder

Musician

Boat

Taxi

Tour guide

Ice-cream van

Bin lorry

Bench

Duck pond

Information desk

Bus

Bus stop

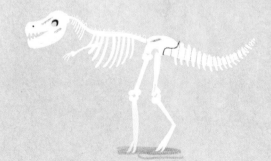
Dinosaur